WATER WHEELS

·AND·HOW·THEY·WORK·

JOHN VINCE

SORBUS

C000225701

CONTENTS

Text & illustrations :
c John Vince · 1993
First published by SORBUS
1993

The moral right of the author has been asserted. All rights reserved. Unauthorised duplication contravenes applicable laws.

·1 S B N · 1 874329 50 8 ·

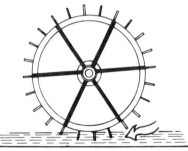

ACKNOWLEDGEMENTS~
Abbeydale Industrial Hamlet, Sheffield.
Castle Museum, York.
Cothele Mill, Cornwall.
Heron Mill, Cumbria.
Forge Mill, Redditch.
Mrs. G. Christiansen, Swanton Mill.
Museum of East Anglian Life, Stowmarket.

INTRODUCTION

WATERPOWER has been used by mankind for some two thousand years. The first watermills were small & probably worked one pair of stones. For many centuries mills were used to grind corn. As early as the C13 however water power was used to work cloth fulling mills. When industry developed in the C18 many heavy tasks were assisted by water power. Early factories had to be located close to a supply of water & this factor determined the siting of such places as Richard Arkwright's cotton mill at Cromford, Derbys.; & the Gregg family's industrial village at Styal, Cheshire.

Forge hammers, fulling stocks, beetling mills, paper mills, snuff mills, gunpowder mills & saw mills all made use of water power.

This book describes the basic machinery of the corn mill, & illustrates some of the other processes which depended upon water power. Many mills have been preserved or restored so that visitors can see how this oldest source of re-newable energy has been used. In most parts of the countryside you can once more find water-driven corn mills which produce stone-ground flour.

HORIZONTAL WHEELS

The earliest watermills in the British Isles worked on a very simple principle. The waterwheel moved in the same plane as the horizontal stones which rotated at the wheel's speed. Horizontal wheels of this kind were used by the Norsemen & their Saxon contemporaries. As the opposite diagram shows water was diverted from a stream [burn] into a wooden channel. The power of the falling water pushed against the vanes of the tirl & caused them to move. The upper end of the wooden tirl supported the runner stone which ground the grain fed into it by the feed shoe. This feed shoe was shaken by the clapper attached to its underside. The vibrating clapper made the grain fall into the eye of the stone. The bedstone did not move. A tenter screw controlled the distance between the two stones. This screw moved the tenter beam upon which the tirl rested.

Reconstructions of horizontal mills can be seen at the Highland Folk Museum, Kingussie; Dounby, Orkney; & at Shawbost, Isle of Lewis.

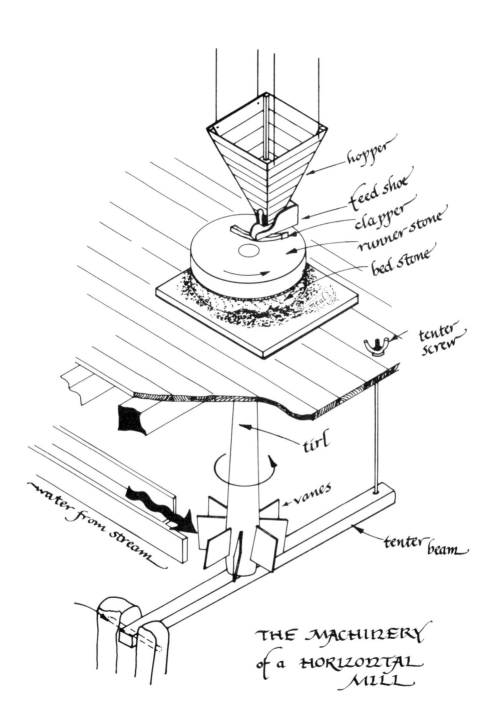

hopper

feed shoe

clapper

runner stone

bed stone

meal

tenter screw

tirl

vanes

water from stream

tenter beam

THE MACHINERY
of a HORIZONTAL
MILL

The simple technology of the horizontal mill was not confined to northern Europe. Examples can be found in Tuscany, in South Africa & in Ireland. Mills of this kind were made from an assortment of materials. As there were few parts it was possible to construct them re-using materials from other buildings or machines.

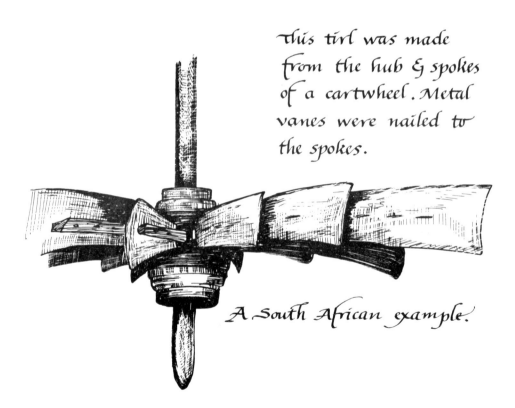

This tirl was made from the hub & spokes of a cartwheel. Metal vanes were nailed to the spokes.

A South African example.

The outfall of the Shawbost mill shows the steep water shoot [x] in the background, the tirl [y] & the tenter beam [z]. The tirl is strengthened by two iron bands [Φ]. These mills could work with a very small water supply.

VERTICAL WHEELS

Vertical waterwheels worked in the following manner. Water was delivered to the paddles or buckets of the wheel via the sluicegate. When the water fell onto a paddle or into a bucket its WEIGHT caused the wheel to move downwards. As the wheel rotated around its axle another paddle/bucket came into contact with the water flowing through the sluice. The wheel continued to move as long as the water flowed.

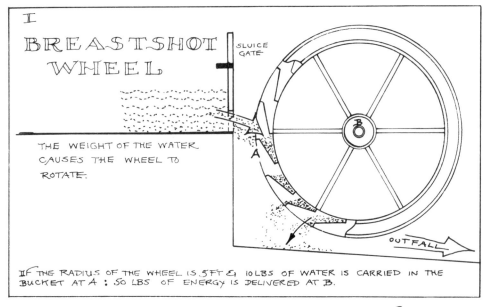

I

BREASTSHOT WHEEL

SLUICE GATE

THE WEIGHT OF THE WATER CAUSES THE WHEEL TO ROTATE.

A

B

OUTFALL

IF THE RADIUS OF THE WHEEL IS 5FT & 10LBS OF WATER IS CARRIED IN THE BUCKET AT A : 50 LBS OF ENERGY IS DELIVERED AT B.

The Roman engineer VITRUVIUS (c. 50 B.C.) first described a vertical water wheel. Early wheels were wooden & their axles were made from squared tree trunks. Some wooden wheels had spokes arranged in clasp-arm fashion: see II opposite.

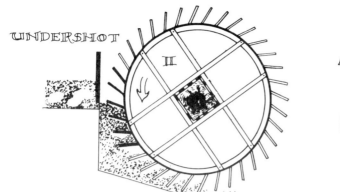

UNDERSHOT

OVERSHOT

There are four kinds of vertical waterwheel. I· BREASTSHOT wheels have the water delivered at or above the centrepoint. II· UNDERSHOT or low breast wheels have a water source below the centre. III· OVERSHOT wheels receive their power from above. IV· PITCHBACK wheels have a high delivery point but turn in the same direction as I & II. Wheels with cast iron rims & iron buckets generate more power than paddle wheels as they hold water for a longer time before it is discharged. The PONCELET, breast shot, wheel was invented by Jean~Victor Poncelet ~ 1788 to 1867. The curved profile of the race added to the wheel's mechanical advantage.

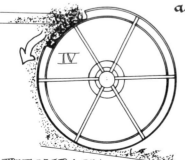

PITCHBACK

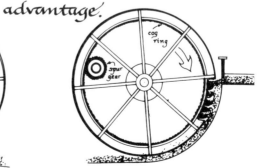

PONCELET

FINCH FOUNDRY,
STICKLEPATH.

THE LAUNDER

An adequate supply of water was essential for every mill. Sometimes it was necessary to bring a supply a considerable distance to a particular mill site. Mill-wrights displayed great ingenuity in constructing a leat, a watercourse, to bring the water to the wheel & sometimes a launder was required. This had to span the air like the aqueducts built by the Romans. The word launder comes from Middle English meaning a water trough. As water is very heavy ~ a cubic foot weighs 62 lbs ~ a launder had to be carefully engineered in order to support a weight of several tons.

Early launders were constructed of timber. From the late C18 cast iron was introduced. Iron aqueducts required strong supports.

COTHELE MILL
CORNWALL

Directing water to the point required was not always easy. This example shows how the watercourse approaches the mill house & then turns sharply just before it reaches the wheel. The stone pillar x carried a great deal of weight.

This overshot waterwheel can be seen at the
Castle Museum, York, where the Raindale Mill
from North Yorkshire has been reconstructed. It
has a single pair of millstones like many of the
small mills in the upland regions. One of
the interesting features of
the fourteen foot diameter
wheel is its offset spokes
which make a Star of
David pattern at the
centre.

· CROMFORD · DERBYS ·

The pitch-back wheel shown here has a distant water source. Pipes are used to bring the supply to the wheel. A cog-ring A around the wheel's edge works a spur gear on a spindle B and in this way energy is transferred to the interior. The village of Cromford is famous as the place where Richard Arkwright established the first successful water-powered cotton mill. Its industrial heritage is being restored by the Arkwright Society & parts of his first mill site are now open to visitors.

THE GEAR TRAIN

Power from the waterwheel was transferred to the inside of the mill by a large gear wheel mounted on the same axle. This wheel is called the PIT WHEEL as half of its form lies below floor level. Most remaining pit wheels are made of cast iron, & some have wooden teeth [cogs]. This pit wheel was made to fit a square axle.

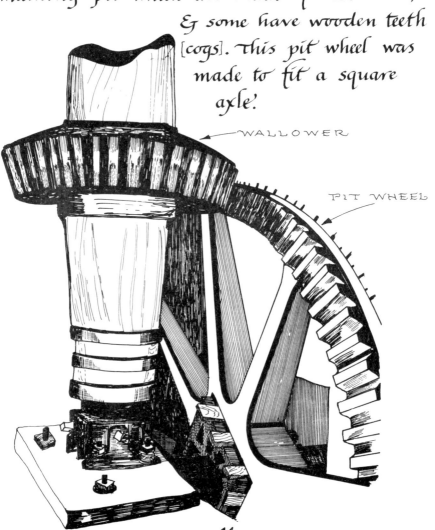

WALLOWER

PIT WHEEL

WALLOWER

PIT
WHEEL

A

B

C

Some mills used the power derived from the pit wheel
to provide a secondary drive for ancillary machinery.
At HERON MILL, Cumbria a second bevel gear [A]
drives a pulley [B] which operates additional
machinery on the floor above via a belt [C].

The train of gears employed to translate the vertical
motion of the waterwheel into the horizontal plane of
the stones was unchanged for more than a thousand
years. Wood was the basic material used by the early
millwrights & it was supplemented with wrought
iron which strengthened moving parts where stress
was greatest. In the C18 cast iron allowed the const-
ruction of lighter components. It became common for
iron cogs to work against wooden teeth as this allowed
for smoother running. The opposite drawing shows how the
gear train worked: The sluice gate 1 controls the water
supply to the overshot wheel 2 . As the axle 3 turns, the
pit wheel 4 moves at the same speed . The wallower 5,
worked by the pit wheel, turns the shaft 12 . This
rotates the spur wheel 7 which operates the stone nut 8 .
The upper runner stone 10 moves at the same speed
as the stone nut . The stones are protected by a wooden
case ~ called a vat or tun ~ & on this rests the hopper
11 . Near the top of the shaft there is a crown wheel 13
which works the belt drive 14 to the sack hoist 15 .
All the machinery was worked by the waterwheel . If
the wheel was not in motion the stones would not
turn & the sack hoist did not work.

DRAWING.
MUSEUM OF EAST
ANGLIAN LIFE.

This sectional view of ALTON WATERMILL shows
how the different working parts relate to one another.
The trap doors of the sack hoist are placed so that the
one rope serves each floor.

GRINDING

To those unfamiliar with milling a first visit to a working mill is something of a mystery. The purpose of all the heavy machinery & the steady beat of the wheel is to change each grain into meal. Millers relied upon gravity to help them perform this task. First of all the sacks of grain were taken up to the top of the mill & emptied into the large bins. From the bin floor the grain passed through a chute & into a hopper. Then it trickled into the shoe which was agitated by the revolving damsel. The grain then fell into the stone's eye where it came into contact with the cutting edges of the rotating stone. Ground grain was expelled around the stone's circumference where it fell into the meal chute & then into the meal bin, or ark, on the floor below. The moving runner stone was protected by a casing called a vat or tun. Upon the tun rested the horse which supported the hopper & feedshoe. A crook string was placed near the meal bin on the floor below. It was attached to the slipper & to a turnpeg. Pressure on the crook string changed the angle of the shoe & altered the amount of grain falling into the stone.

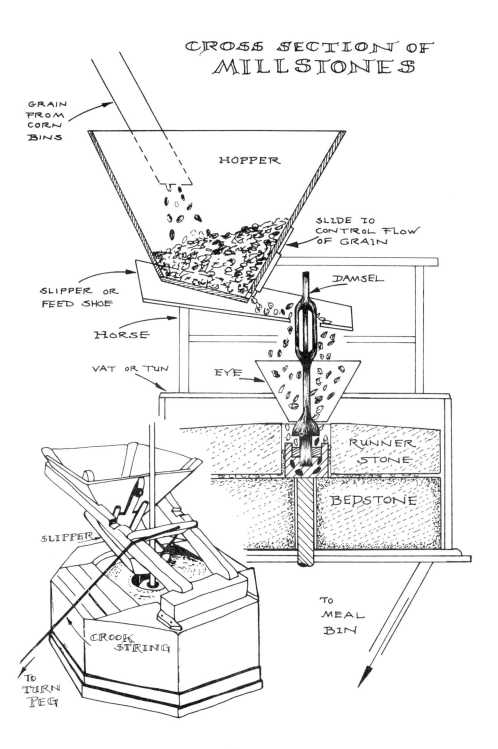

CROSS SECTION OF MILLSTONES

GRAIN FROM CORN BINS

HOPPER

SLIDE TO CONTROL FLOW OF GRAIN

SLIPPER OR FEED SHOE

DAMSEL

HORSE

VAT OR TUN

EYE

RUNNER STONE

BEDSTONE

SLIPPER

CROOK STRING

TO TURN PEG

TO MEAL BIN

MILLSTONES

HARP

Millstones were used in pairs.
Carefully made grooves were
cut into the face of each
stone. The cut faces rotated
against each other in order
to grind the grain. The design
of the grooves was made in a
methodical way. A template guided
the stone dresser when marking
out a new stone with his mill bill.
Two kinds of stone were used in
most mills. Derbyshire Peak stones
were used for grinding grist for
cattle feed. French Burr stones
were used for flour. Stones had to
run evenly & most had a blob
or two of lead added to the
upper face of the runner stone
for the same reason we add weights
to a car wheel.

MILL
BILL

FRENCH BURR STONES
WERE MADE FROM IRREGULARLY CUT
SECTIONS BOUND WITH IRON BANDS.

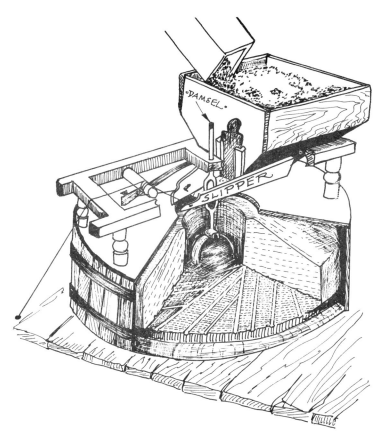

This sectional view of the stones shows how the damsel shakes the slipper and causes the grain to fall into the eye of the stone. As the upper stone turns the grooves in the stones' faces pass one another and create a scissor~like action which reduces the grain to a fine powder. Centrifugal force expels the flour or meal around the outer edge & it falls into the flour chute. Freshly ground flour feels warm.

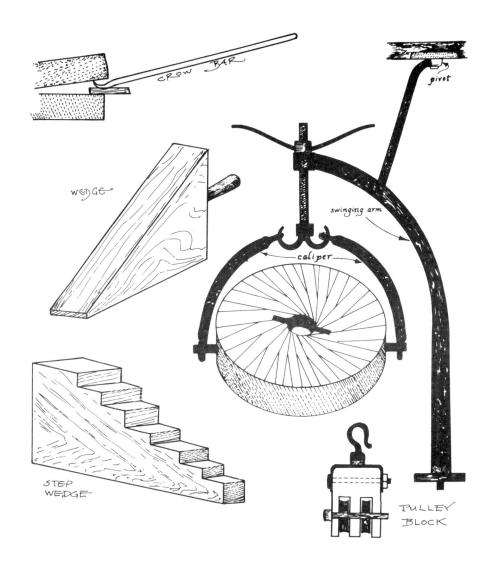

CROW BAR

pivot

WEDGE

swinging arm

caliper

STEP WEDGE

PULLEY BLOCK

Moving a heavy millstone weighing several hundredweights was not an easy task. Various mechanical aids were used to raise & turn over a stone ready for dressing. Apart from wedges & levers some mills had a stone-crane which raised the stone by means of a screw jack.

PUMPING MILLS

Waterwheels were often used to pump water. This example shows the spectacular ~72 ft 6 ins. diameter~ pumping wheel at Laxey, Isle of Man.

TILT HAMMERS

WATER was an essential source of power when industry began to develop in the C18. Many factories which produced ironwork needed water to work the heavy tilt hammers like the ones shown above. The water wheel shared its axle [A] with the large clasp-arm wheel [B]. The gears on this wheel moved the gears & flywheel [C]. As this turned the heavy tappet wheels [D], each hammer [E] would rise & fall upon the anvils [F]. Working in such a factory was noisy & dangerous. This machinery, now nearly two hundred years old, can be seen at the Abbeydale Industrial Hamlet, Sheffield. Other similar hammers can be seen at Wortley Top Forge, Sheffield & at the Finch Foundry, Sticklepath, Devon.

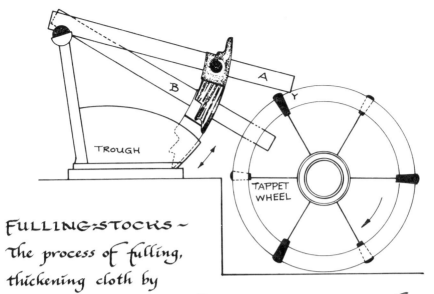

FULLING-STOCKS ~

The process of fulling, thickening cloth by pounding, made use of a tappet wheel. This lifted the fulling stocks A+B as it revolved ~ three times at each revolution. When each tappet reached y the stock could fall into the trough containing the cloth.

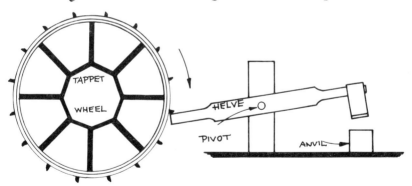

The diagram above shows how a tail operated TILT HAMMER worked. As the tappet wheel turns it causes the hammer to strike 16 times per revolution.

BLOWING ENGINES

At the forge air was essential to provide the correct heat. Country blacksmiths used hand bellows, but a constant supply of blown air was needed when tilt hammers were operated. The blowing engine opposite was constructed c. 1800, & it can still be seen at the Abbeydale Industrial Hamlet, Sheffield. The axle of the waterwheel turned the triangular cams. Upon them rested the riding wheels [A] which moved up & down as the axle rotated. This motion pushed

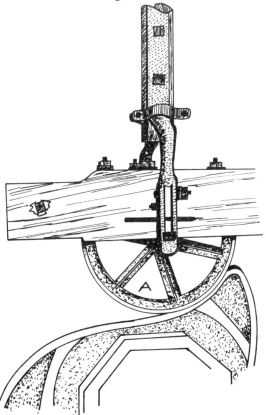

the piston rods which moved inside the air cylinders. Each piston sucked in air on a down-stroke & expelled it on the upstroke. Pipes fed the air into the working hearths.

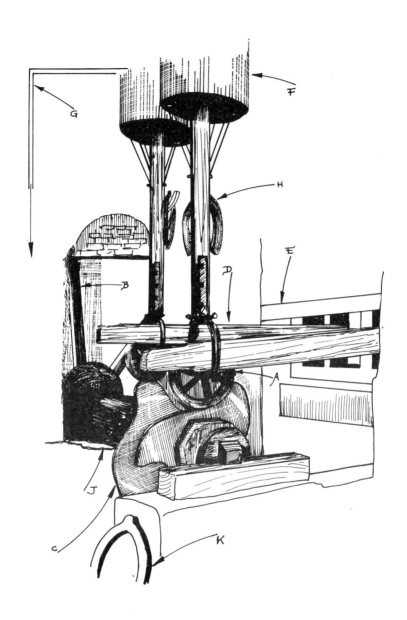

A— RIDING WHEEL · B— WATERWHEEL · C— TRIANGULAR CAMS·
D—BEAMS · E— ANCHOR FRAME TO PIVOT D · F—CYLINDERS·
G— AIR PIPES TO HEARTHS · H—COUNTERWEIGHTS TO PULL
AGAINST SUCTION · J— WHEEL'S AXLE · K—SPARE WEIGHT.

NEEDLE MILLS

NEEDLES were a very important commodity & they were used in many different trades. A needle starts life as a piece of wire. After it has been given an eye and a point it has to be polished. This process of polishing was eventually mechanised. Waterpower was used to roll the needles to & fro beneath a heavy platen. The needles were first packed in bundles with a mixture of soap and abrasive powder. They were wrapped in a long sausage-shaped roll of hurden, a coarse fabric, & tightly bound. The action of rolling the bundles caused the needles to rub against one another. After some 25 hours of SCOURING, as the process was called, the needles were ready for cleaning & packing.

This diagram shows how the spur wheel A, powered by the waterwheel, works a secondary gear B which operates a crankshaft C. As this rotates the connecting rod D rocks the rocking arm E. The curved arm F is attached to the platen G which moves backwards & forwards in unison with the rocking arm. The two hurdens H under the platen roll upon the scouring bed J.

Each hurden was rolled about 35,000 times in a day.

The rocking arm also worked scouring beds on the floor above.

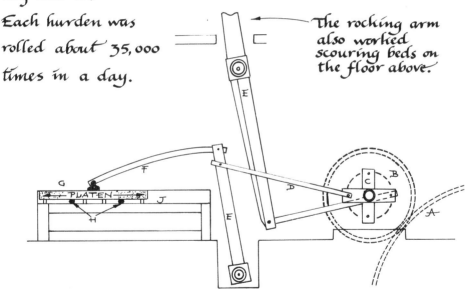

Forge Mill, Redditch, Worcs., is an C18 needle mill which remained in production until 1958. It is now an important museum of needle making.

TIDE MILLS

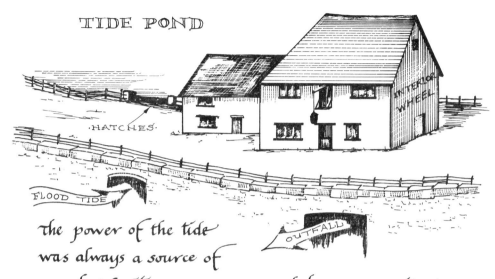

TIDE POND

·HATCHES·

INTERIOR WHEEL

FLOOD TIDE

OUTFALL

The power of the tide was always a source of wonder & its energy was used by man centuries ago. Once there were many mills worked by the tide around England & Wales. Machinery inside a tide mill was just the same as any other watermill. The difference was in the way the water power was obtained. In place of a running stream the tide miller had to fill the mill pond each time the tide came in. To enable the miller to work the mill continuously between tides one-way hatches allowed tide water to enter the pond. As the tide ebbed the trapped water created a 'head' which provided power when it was released to work the wheel. Between each tide the miller had a few hours to work before the flood tide returned.

MILL BUILDINGS

SWANTON MILL, KENT.

In the mediaeval period most villages had a mill. Some present day mills occupy sites known to have been in use in 1086 ~ when the Domesday Book was compiled. The right to own a mill in feudal times was restricted to the Lord of the Manor. All tenants were obliged to have their corn ground at the Lord's mill & he took part of their flour in payment.

The materials used to build a mill depended upon its location. Local materials were used to construct the early mills. Many mills, like the one above, had extra sections added to the original structure. That is why so many are now large & rambling buildings. The overhanging part [A] is called a LUCAM. It contained the sack hoist.

The Cotswold mill shown above is a stone building augmented with a brick & slate extension linking it to a formerly detached stone barn. This building is an example of the way the development of the canals & railways allowed building materials to be 'imported' from other regions. Brick & slate buildings can now be seen in areas which traditionally used stone or timber & thatch.

A list of mills open to the public can be found in: Discovering Watermills ~ Shire Publications.